ROALD DAHL'S

MARVELLOUS MISS HONEY

working in
partnership
with

National
Literacy
Trust

ILLUSTRATED BY QUENTIN BLAKE

PUFFIN

PUFFIN BOOKS

UK | USA | Canada | Ireland | Australia
India | New Zealand | South Africa

Puffin Books is part of the Penguin Random House group of companies
whose addresses can be found at global.penguinrandomhouse.com.

www.penguin.co.uk   www.puffin.co.uk   www.ladybird.co.uk

Made for McDonald's 2017
001

Matilda: first published by Jonathan Cape 1988
Published in paperback by Puffin Books

Printed in Slovakia

A CIP catalogue record for this book is available from the British Library

ISBN: 978-0-141-38633-1

The National Literacy Trust is a registered charity no. 1116260 and a company limited
by guarantee no. 5836486 registered in England and Wales and a registered charity in
Scotland no. SC042944. Registered address: 68 South Lambeth Road, London SW8 1RL.
National Literacy Trust logo and reading tips copyright © National Literacy Trust, 2017
www.literacytrust.org.uk/donate

Batch nr: 128351/16

FSC
MIX
FSC® C022120

Meet
MARVELLOUS
MISS HONEY !

MISS HONEY is the **LOVELIEST** teacher you could ever **HOPE TO KNOW!**

Turn to the back of your book for **STICKERS** and a handy **BOOKMARK**

READ ON to get a glimpse into what happens when she meets a **VERY CLEVER** little girl called **MATILDA . . .**

SEARCH and FIND!

When Miss Honey visits Mr and Mrs Wormwood, **WHAT COLOUR IS HER COAT?**

MISS HONEY

Matilda Wormwood was a little late in starting school. Most children begin Primary School at five or even just before, but Matilda's parents, who weren't very concerned one way or the other about their daughter's education, had forgotten to make the proper arrangements in advance. She was five and a half when she entered school for the first time.

Naturally Matilda was put in the bottom class, where there were eighteen other small boys and girls about the same age as her. Their teacher was called Miss Honey, and she could not have been more than twenty-three or twenty-four. She had a lovely pale oval madonna face with blue eyes and her hair was light-brown. Her body was so slim and fragile one got the feeling that if she fell over she would smash into a thousand pieces, like a porcelain figure.

Miss Jennifer Honey was a mild and quiet person who never raised her voice and was seldom seen to smile, but there is no doubt she possessed that rare gift for being adored by every small child under her care. She seemed to understand totally the bewilderment and fear that so often overwhelm young children who for the first time in their lives are herded into a classroom and told to obey orders. Some curious warmth that was almost tangible shone out of Miss Honey's face when she spoke to a confused and homesick newcomer to the class.

After the usual business of going through all the names of the children, Miss Honey handed out a brand-new exercise-book to each pupil.

'You have all brought your own pencils, I hope,' she said.

'Yes, Miss Honey,' they chanted.

'Good. Now this is the very first day of school for each one of you. It is the beginning of at least eleven long years of schooling that all of you are going to have to go through. And six of those years will be spent right here at Crunchem Hall. I want to help you to learn as much as possible while you are in this class. That is because I know it will make things easier for you later on. For example, by the end of this week I shall expect every one of you to know the two-times table by heart. And in a year's time I hope you will know all the multiplication tables up to twelve. It will help you enormously if you do. Now then, do any of you happen to have learnt the two-times table already?'

Matilda put up her hand. She was the only one.

Miss Honey looked carefully at the tiny girl with dark hair and a round serious face sitting in the second row. 'Wonderful,' she said. 'Please stand up and recite as much of it as you can.'

Matilda stood up and began to say the two-times table. When she got to twice twelve is twenty-four she didn't stop. She went right on with twice thirteen is twenty-six, twice fourteen is twenty-eight, twice fifteen is thirty, twice sixteen is . . .

'Stop!' Miss Honey said. She had been listening slightly spellbound to this smooth recital, and now she said, 'How far can you go?'

'How far?' Matilda said. 'Well, I don't really know, Miss Honey. For quite a long way, I think.'

Miss Honey took a few moments to let this curious statement sink in. 'You mean,' she said, 'that you could tell me what two times twenty-eight is?'

'Yes, Miss Honey.'

'What is it?'

'Fifty-six, Miss Honey.'

'What about something much harder, like two times four hundred and eighty-seven? Could you tell me that?'

'I think so, yes,' Matilda said.

'What is it then, two times four hundred and eighty-seven?'

'Nine hundred and seventy-four,' Matilda said immediately. She spoke quietly and politely and without any sign of showing off.

Miss Honey gazed at Matilda with absolute amazement, but

when next she spoke she kept her voice level. 'That is really splendid,' she said. 'But of course multiplying by two is a lot easier than some of the bigger numbers. What about the other multiplication tables? Do you know any of those?'

Colour me in!

'I think so, Miss Honey. I think I do.'

'Which ones, Matilda? How far have you got?'

'I . . . I don't quite know,' Matilda said.

11

'I don't know what you mean.'

'What I mean is do you for instance know the three-times table?'

'Yes, Miss Honey.'

'And the four-times?'

'Yes, Miss Honey.'

'Well, how many *do* you know, Matilda? Do you know all the way up to the twelve-times table?'

'Yes, Miss Honey.'

'What are twelve sevens?'

'Eighty-four,' Matilda said.

Miss Honey paused and leaned back in her chair behind the plain table that stood in the middle of the floor in front of the class. She was considerably shaken by this exchange but took care not to show it. She had never come across a five-year-old before, or indeed a ten-year-old, who could multiply with such facility.

'I hope the rest of you are listening to this,' she said to the class. 'Matilda is a very lucky girl. She has wonderful parents who have already taught her to multiply lots of numbers. Was it your mother, Matilda, who taught you?'

'No, Miss Honey, it wasn't.'

'You must have a great father then. He must be a brilliant teacher.'

'No, Miss Honey,' Matilda said quietly. 'My father did not teach me.'

'You mean you taught yourself?'

Colour me in!

'I don't quite know,' Matilda said truthfully. 'It's just that I don't find it very difficult to multiply one number by another.'

14

Miss Honey took a deep breath and let it out slowly. She looked again at the small girl with bright eyes standing beside her desk so sensible and solemn. 'You say you don't find it difficult to multiply one number by another,' Miss Honey said. 'Could you try to explain that a little bit? Could you try to tell me exactly what goes on inside your head when you get a multiplication to do? You obviously have to work it out in some way, but you seem able to arrive at the answer almost instantly.'

'I'm afraid I don't know how to explain it,' Matilda said. 'I've always said to myself that if a little pocket calculator can do it why shouldn't I?'

'Why not indeed?' Miss Honey said. 'The human brain is an amazing thing.'

'I think it's a lot better than a lump of metal,' Matilda said. 'That's all a calculator is.'

'How right you are,' Miss Honey said. 'Pocket calculators are not allowed in this school anyway.' Miss Honey was feeling quite quivery. There was no doubt in her mind that she had met a truly extraordinary mathematical brain, and words like child-genius and prodigy went flitting through her head. She knew that these sorts of wonders do pop up in the world from time to time, but only once or twice in a hundred years. After all, Mozart was only five when he started composing for the piano and look what happened to him.

BREAK TIME!

Colour in all the letters marked '1'
to reveal Matilda's favourite hobby!

Answer on page 62

At this point Miss Honey could not resist the temptation of exploring still further the mind of this astonishing child. She knew that she ought to be paying some attention to the rest of the class but she was altogether too excited to let the matter rest.

'Well,' she said, pretending to address the whole class, 'let us leave sums for the moment and see if any

of you have begun to learn to spell.
Hands up anyone who can spell *cat*.'

Three hands went up. They
belonged to a girl called Lavender, a
small boy called Nigel and to Matilda.

'Spell *cat*, Nigel.'

Nigel spelled it.

Miss Honey now decided to ask a
question that normally she would not
have dreamed of asking the class on its
first day. 'I wonder,' she said, 'whether
any of you three who know how to
spell *cat* have learnt how to read a

whole group of words when they are strung together in a sentence?'

'I have,' Nigel said.

'So have I,' Lavender said.

Miss Honey went to the blackboard and wrote with her white chalk the sentence, *I have already begun to learn how to read long sentences.* She had purposely made it difficult and she knew that there were precious few five-year-olds around who would be able to manage it.

'Can you tell me what that says, Nigel?' she asked.

'That's too hard,' Nigel said.

'Lavender?'

'The first word is I,' Lavender said.

'Can any of you read the whole sentence?' Miss Honey asked, waiting for the 'yes' that she felt certain was going to come from Matilda.

'Yes,' Matilda said.

'Go ahead,' Miss Honey said.

Matilda read the sentence without any hesitation at all.

'That really is very good indeed,' Miss Honey said, making the understatement of her life. 'How much *can* you read, Matilda?'

'I think I can read most things, Miss Honey,' Matilda said, 'although I'm afraid I can't always understand the meanings.'

Miss Honey got to her feet and walked smartly out of the room, but was back in thirty seconds carrying a thick book. She opened it at random and placed it on Matilda's desk.

'This is a book of humorous poetry,' she said. 'See if you can read that one aloud.'

Smoothly, without a pause and at a nice speed, Matilda began to read:

'An epicure dining at Crewe
Found a rather large mouse in his stew.
Cried the waiter, "Don't shout
And wave it about
Or the rest will be wanting one too."'

Several children saw the funny side of the rhyme and laughed. Miss Honey said, 'Do you know what an epicure is, Matilda?'

'It is someone who is dainty with his eating,' Matilda said.

'That is correct,' Miss Honey said. 'And do you happen to know what that particular type of poetry is called?'

'It's called a limerick,' Matilda said. 'That's a lovely one. It's so funny.'

Colour us in!

'It's a famous one,' Miss Honey said, picking up the book and returning to her table in front of the class. 'A witty limerick is very hard to write,' she added. 'They look easy but they most certainly are not.'

'I know,' Matilda said. 'I've tried quite a few times but mine are never any good.'

'You have, have you?' Miss Honey said, more startled than ever. 'Well, Matilda, I would very much like to hear one of these limericks you say you have written. Could you try to remember one for us?'

'Well,' Matilda said, hesitating, 'I've actually been trying to make up one about you, Miss Honey, while we've been sitting here.'

'About *me*!' Miss Honey cried. 'Well, we've certainly got to hear that one, haven't we?'

'I don't think I want to say it, Miss Honey.'

'Please tell it,' Miss Honey said. 'I promise I won't mind.'

'I think you will, Miss Honey, because I have to use your first name to make things rhyme and that's why I don't want to say it.'

'How do you know my first name?' Miss Honey asked.

'I heard another teacher calling you by it just before we came in,' Matilda said. 'She called you Jenny.'

'I insist upon hearing this limerick,' Miss Honey said, smiling one of her rare smiles. 'Stand up and recite it.'

Reluctantly Matilda stood up and very slowly, very nervously, she recited her limerick:

'The thing we all ask about Jenny
Is, "Surely there cannot be many
Young girls in the place
With so lovely a face?"
The answer to that is, "*Not any!*"'

The whole of Miss Honey's pale and pleasant face blushed a brilliant scarlet. Then once again she smiled. It was a

much broader one this time, a smile
of pure pleasure.

'Why, thank you, Matilda,' she said,
still smiling. 'Although it is not true, it is
really a very good limerick. Oh dear, oh
dear, I must try to remember that one.'

From the third row of desks,
Lavender said, 'It's good. I like it.'

'It's true as well,' a small boy
called Rupert said.

'Of course it's true,' Nigel said.

Already the whole class had
begun to warm towards

Miss Honey, although as yet she had hardly taken any notice of any of them except Matilda.

'Who taught you to read, Matilda?' Miss Honey asked.

'I just sort of taught myself, Miss Honey.'

'And have you read any books all by yourself, any children's books, I mean?'

'I've read all the ones that are in the public library in the High Street, Miss Honey.'

'And did you like them?'

'I liked some of them very much indeed,' Matilda said, 'but I thought others were fairly dull.'

'Do you think that all children's books ought to have funny bits in them?' Miss Honey asked.

'I do,' Matilda said. 'Children are not so serious as grown-ups and they love to laugh.'

Miss Honey was astounded by the wisdom of this tiny girl. She said, 'And what are you going to do now that you've read all the children's books?'

'I am reading other books,' Matilda said. 'I borrow them from the library. Mrs Phelps is very kind to me. She helps me to choose them.'

Miss Honey was leaning far forward over her work-table and gazing in wonder at the child. She had completely forgotten now about the rest of the class. 'What other books?' she murmured.

'I am very fond of Charles Dickens,' Matilda said.

'He makes me laugh a lot. Especially Mr Pickwick.'

At that moment the bell in the corridor sounded for the end of class.

CROSSWORD

Are you a great reader like Matilda? Complete the sentences below and fill in the grid on the next page with your answers.

1 DOWN: Matilda recites a poem called a _ _ _ _ r _ _ _ to describe Miss Honey. (Hint: p.30)

2 ACROSS: Matilda is _ _ v _ and a half years old when she starts school. (Hint: p.2)

3 DOWN: Matilda overhears that Miss Honey's first name is _ _ _ _ y. (Hint: p.29)

4 ACROSS: Someone who is 'dainty with their eating' is called an _ _ _ c _ _ _. (Hint: p.26)

5 ACROSS: According to Miss Honey, the human brain is an _ m _ _ _ _ _ thing! (Hint: p.16)

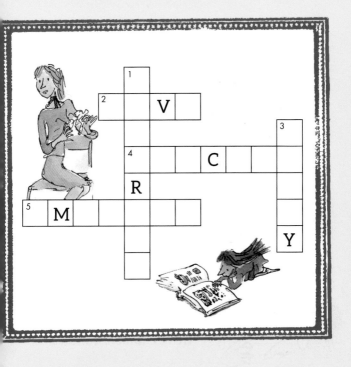

Answers on page 62

MISS HONEY MAKES A PLAN

Miss Honey decided that she would go and have a talk with Matilda's mother and father as soon as possible. She couldn't believe that the parents had had no part in developing their daughter's remarkable talents. After all, Mr Wormwood was a successful motor-car dealer so she presumed that he was a fairly intelligent man himself. In any event, parents never *underestimated* the abilities of their own children. Quite the reverse. Sometimes it was well nigh impossible for a teacher to convince the proud father or mother that their beloved offspring was a complete nitwit. Miss Honey felt confident that she would have no difficulty in convincing Mr and Mrs Wormwood that Matilda was something very special indeed. The trouble was going to be to stop them from getting over-enthusiastic.

And now Miss Honey's hopes began to expand even further. She started wondering whether permission might not be sought from the parents for her to give private tuition to Matilda after school. The prospect of coaching a child as bright as this appealed enormously to her professional instinct as a teacher. And suddenly she decided that she would go and call on Mr and Mrs Wormwood that very evening. She would go fairly late when Matilda was sure to be in bed.

And that is precisely what she did. Having got the address from the

school records, Miss Honey set out
to walk from her own home to the
Wormwoods' house shortly after nine.
It was a modern brick house that could
not have been cheap to buy and the
name on the gate said COSY NOOK.
Nosey cook might have been better, Miss
Honey thought. She was given to
playing with words in that way.
She walked up the path and
rang the bell, and while she
stood waiting she could hear the
television blaring inside.

The door was opened by a small ratty-looking man with a thin ratty moustache who was wearing a sports-coat that had an orange and red stripe in the material. 'Yes?' he said, peering out at Miss Honey.

'Please forgive me for butting in on you like this,' Miss Honey said. 'I am Matilda's teacher at school and it is important I have a word with you and your wife.'

'Got into trouble already, has she?' Mr Wormwood said, blocking

the doorway. 'Well, she's your
responsibility from now on. You'll have
to deal with her.'

'She is in no trouble at all,' Miss Honey said. 'I have come with good news about her. Quite startling news, Mr Wormwood. Do you think I might come in for a few minutes and talk to you about Matilda?'

'We are right in the middle of watching one of our favourite programmes,' Mr Wormwood said. 'This is most inconvenient. Why don't you come back some other time?'

Miss Honey began to lose patience. 'Mr Wormwood,' she said, 'if you think some rotten TV programme is more important than your daughter's future, then you ought not to be a parent! Why don't you switch the darn thing off and listen to me!'

That shook Mr Wormwood. He was not used to being spoken to in this way. He peered carefully at the slim frail woman who stood so resolutely out on the porch. 'Oh very well then,' he snapped. 'Come on in and let's get it over with.' Miss Honey stepped briskly inside.

SPOT THE DIFFERENCE

Can you spot five differences between these two pictures of Miss Honey and Mr Wormwood?

Answers on page 62

THE PARENTS

'Mrs Wormwood isn't going to thank you for this,' the man said as he led Miss Honey into the sitting-room, where a large platinum-blonde woman was gazing rapturously at the TV screen.

'Who is it?' the woman said, not looking round.

'Some school teacher,' Mr Wormwood said. 'She says she's got to talk to us about Matilda.' He crossed to the TV set and turned down the sound but left the picture on the screen.

'Don't do that, Harry!' Mrs Wormwood cried out. 'Willard is just about to propose to Angelica!'

'You can still watch it while we're talking,' Mr Wormwood said. 'This is Matilda's teacher. She says she's got some sort of news to give us.'

'My name is Jennifer Honey,' Miss Honey said. 'How do you do, Mrs Wormwood.'

Mrs Wormwood glared at her and said, 'What's the trouble then?'

Nobody invited Miss Honey to sit down so she chose a chair and sat down anyway. 'This,' she said, 'was your daughter's first day at school.'

'We know that,' Mrs Wormwood said, ratty about missing her programme. 'Is that all you came to tell us?'

'I'm sure you know,' Miss Honey said, 'that children in the bottom class at school are not expected to be able to read or spell or juggle with numbers when they first arrive. Five-year-olds cannot do that. But Matilda can do it all. And if I am to believe her . . .'

'I wouldn't,' Mrs Wormwood said. She was still ratty at losing the sound on the TV.

'Was she lying, then,' Miss Honey said, 'when she told me that nobody taught

her to multiply or to read? Did either of you teach her?'

'Teach her what?' Mr Wormwood said.

'To read. To read books,' Miss Honey said. 'Perhaps you *did* teach her. Perhaps she *was* lying. Perhaps you have shelves full of books all over the house. I wouldn't know. Perhaps you are both great readers.'

'Of course we read,' Mr Wormwood said. 'Don't be so daft. I read the *Autocar* and the

Motor from cover to cover every week.'

'This child has already read an astonishing number of books,' Miss Honey said. 'I was simply trying to find out if she came from a family that loved good literature.'

'We don't hold with book-reading,' Mr Wormwood said. 'You can't make a living from sitting on your backside and reading story-books. We don't keep them in the house.'

'I see,' Miss Honey said. 'Well, all I came to tell you was that Matilda has a brilliant mind. But I expect you knew that already.'

'Of course I knew she could read,' the mother said. 'She spends her life up in her room buried in some silly book.'

'But does it not intrigue you,' Miss Honey said,

'that a little five-year-old child is reading long adult novels by Dickens and Hemingway? Doesn't that make you jump up and down with excitement?'

'Not particularly,' the mother said. 'I'm not in favour of blue-stocking girls. A girl should think about making herself look attractive so she can get a good husband later on. Looks is more important than books, Miss Hunky . . .'

'The name is Honey,' Miss Honey said.

'Now look at *me*,' Mrs Wormwood

said. 'Then look at *you*. You chose
books. I chose looks.'

Miss Honey looked at the plain plump person with the smug suet-pudding face who was sitting across the room. 'What did you say?' she asked.

'I said you chose books and I chose looks,' Mrs Wormwood said. 'And who's finished up the better off? Me, of course. I'm sitting pretty in a nice house with a successful businessman and you're left slaving away teaching a lot of nasty little children the ABC.'

'I can see we're not going to agree. I'm sorry I burst in on you like this.'

Miss Honey rose from her chair and walked out of the room.

Mr Wormwood followed her to the front-door and said, 'Good of you to come, Miss Hawkes, or is it Miss Harris?'

'It's neither,' Miss Honey said, 'but let it go.' And away she went.

MARVELLOUS MEMORY CHALLENGE

Study this picture, then cover it up.

How many of the
questions below
can you answer?

a. Where is Mr Wormwood standing?

. . . .

b. What colour is Mr Wormwood's jacket?

. . . .

c. What jewellery is Mrs Wormwood wearing?

. . . .

Answers on page 62

Use your
stickers to bring
this scene
to life!

ANSWERS

P.1: SEARCH AND FIND

Miss Honey's coat is blue.

P.18: BREAK TIME!

R E A D I N G

P.36: CROSSWORD

		¹L				
²F	I	V	E			
		M			³J	
⁴E	P	I	C	U	R	E
		R			E	
⁵A	M	A	Z	I	N	G
		C			N	
		K			Y	

1 DOWN: LIMERICK; **2 ACROSS:** FIVE;
3 DOWN: JENNY; **4 ACROSS:** EPICURE;
5 ACROSS: AMAZING

P.46: SPOT THE DIFFERENCE

P.59 MARVELLOUS MEMORY CHALLENGE

a. Mr Wormwood is standing behind Mrs Wormwood's chair.

b. Mr Wormwood's jacket is orange and red.

c. Mrs Wormwood is wearing a necklace, earrings and bracelets.

ROALD
DAHL